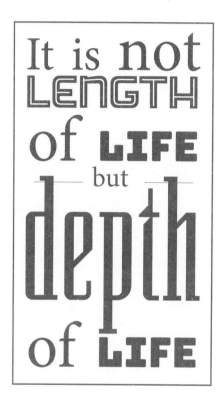

It is not LENGTH of LIFE but depth of LIFE

Ralph Waldo Emerson

Together with friends
these memories are built,
together with *joy*,
together with *sorrow*,
together with *laughter*
and **together tomorrow.**

Welcome, friends, thank you
for joining us on this occasion

Name

Comments

Name

Comments

Name

Comments

Name

Comments

Name

Comments

Name

Comments

Name

Comments

Name

Comments

Name

Comments

Name

Comments

Name

Comments

Name

Comments

Name

Comments

Name

Comments

Name

Comments

Name

Comments

Name

Comments

Name   *Comments*

Name

Comments

Name

Comments

Name

Comments

Name

Comments

Name

Comments

Name

Comments

Name

Comments

Name

Comments

Name

Comments

Name

Comments

Name

Comments

Name   Comments

Name

Comments

Name

Comments

Name

Comments

Name

Comments

Name

Comments

Name

Comments

Name

Comments

Name

Comments

Name

Comments

Name

Comments

Name

Comments

Name

Comments

Name

Comments

Name

Comments

Name

Comments

Name

Comments

Name

Comments

Name

Comments

Name

Comments

Name

Comments